TestingMom.com's

Complete Practice Test for New York City G&T Program Includes Preparation For NNAT ® and OLSAT ®

For Pre-K and Kindergarten Students (Kindergarten and First Grade Entry)

Website

- Online test prep your child will love!

- INSTANT access to over 100,000 printable practice questions, practice tests, interactive games and more – all of which feel like fun – not like boring test prep!

- Access to 40+ top educational programs so your child can build skills in math, reading, ELA, science, social studies, chess and keyboarding (over $500 value).

- Use our Digital Tutor tool to assess and track your child's progress for the New York City Gifted and Talented Test.

- Your child will go into the New York City Gifted and Talented Test with the confidence needed to perform at their best!

- Get started for free today. Go to www.TestingMom.com.

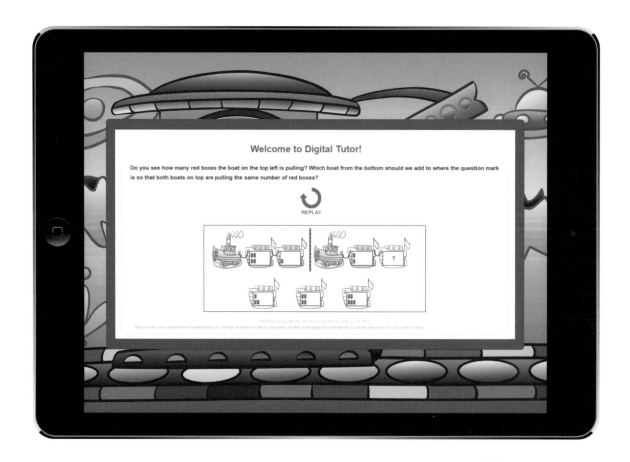

Flashcards

- Sold separately. Available at www.TestingMom.com/Store and on Amazon.com.

IQ Fun Pack

- Prepare your child for the New York City Gifted and Talented Test in a way that feels like play!
- Looks and feels like a game, but it's really a complete test prep system for OLSAT® and NNAT®. Makes test prep painless for parents and fun for kids!
- 25 games-in-one, over 11,000 learning challenges, flashcards, and more.
- Sold separately. Available at www.TestingMom.com/Store.

Table of Contents

Note: All questions on this practice test are original TestingMom.com questions. They are not the actual questions that are on the OLSAT or NNAT.

New York City Gifted & Talented Testing
If you are reading this, then you are a parent or a grandparent in New York City who is trying to find the best possible school for your little one. There are so many options in New York City – private schools, gifted and talented programs, general education – it can sometimes feel overwhelming, especially if your child is just 4-years-old!

In New York City, there are two types of free Gifted & Talented programs available to students who qualify via the New York City Department of Education: 1) The City-wide program and 2) the District-wide program. For detailed information, go to: http://schools.nyc.gov/ChoicesEnrollment/GiftedandTalented/

1. **Tests Required for City-wide and District-wide Qualification**
   a. Children will take:
      i. Naglieri Nonverbal Ability Test® (NNAT® test), a non-verbal test, 48 questions which count for 50% of the child's composite score.
      ii. Verbal Portion only of the Otis Lennon School Ability Test® (OLSAT®), 30 questions which count for 50% of the child's composite score.

   b. Scoring:
      i. Your child will be given a nationally normed percentile rank for the OLSAT test and for the NNAT test.
      ii. Then, these two scores will be combined into a single percentile score that will be normed against other NYC students.
      iii. **City-wide qualification** – A child must score in the 97th percentile to be eligible for the City-wide program. In the last few years (due to space limitations), only children who scored in the 99th percentile have been admitted into these programs. The only exception to this is siblings of current students who are admitted with scores of 97th percentile or above.
      iv. **District-wide qualification** – A child must score in the 90th percentile to be eligible for the District-wide program. Depending on the popularity of a given District-wide program, it may require a higher score for a child to get in. The only exception to this is siblings of current students who are admitted with scores of 90th percentile or above.
      v. **Lottery** – If there are several students applying to the same school with the same combined percentile scores, siblings will get first preference and then there will be a lottery for the other students.

NNAT

When your child is tested, the NNAT is given first. All 48 questions are "puzzles" that require visual-spatial reasoning to solve. This test does not require your child to either speak or understand English.

There are 4 types of questions:

Pattern Completion

Each question has a large rectangle with a design or pattern. Within the rectangle, there is a smaller rectangle with a question mark covering a section of the design or pattern. Your child must pick an answer that, if placed over the question mark, would complete the design or pattern.

Reasoning by Analogy

Each question has rows of figures that are related to each other in some way. Your child must identify the relationship between the figures in the row(s) on top. Then, he must choose an answer so that the figures on the bottom relate to each other in same way as the figures on top.

Serial Reasoning

Each question has 3 rows and 3 columns of shapes or figures. Your child must identify the pattern that is taking place across the 3 rows and 3 columns. Then, she must choose an answer that completes the pattern.

Spatial Visualization

There are 2 types of questions in this category. 1) **Combination** - Each question has rows of boxes where the figures in the first box combine with the figures in the second box to create a new design in the third box. Your child must choose an answer that combines the figures in the first and second boxes together (the same way the figures were combined on top) to create a new design in the third box. 2) **Folding Tabs** - Each question has a row of designs with tabs folded out and then folded in. Your child must choose an answer that shows how the design on the bottom would look if the tabs were folded in the same way they were folded in on top.

OLSAT

This part of the test is given second. All 30 questions require your child to use verbal reasoning to answer. The questions on this part of the test are black and white. This part of the test can be given in Arabic, Bengali, Cantonese, Mandarin, English, French, Haitian-Creole, Korean, Russian, Spanish and Urdu.

There are 3 types of questions on the OLSAT:

Following Directions

Verbal questions describing similarities and differences, positional and rank comparisons (above, below, between, next to, bigger, smaller, etc.), or descriptions where the child must choose visual images that fit the description.

Aural Reasoning

Verbal descriptions of scenarios, similarities and differences, prepositions, and situations that use vocabulary or ideas that make the child think in order to choose the visual image that fits the description.

Arithmetic Reasoning

The child must listen carefully to math word problems that use basic mathematical concepts such as same, different, fewer, more, etc., along with simple addition, subtraction, fractions (half, quarter), etc.

If you have specific questions about the NYC Gifted and Talented Program please email us at help@testingmom.com (make sure you mention this workbook).

Skills Required for These Tests
- The questions in the NNAT and OLSAT tests cover cognitive abilities that are not specifically taught in school.

- These are abstract thinking abilities such as problem solving, classifying and categorizing, recognizing patterns and sequences, reasoning with shapes and figures, deductive and inductive reasoning, mathematical reasoning and more.

- For pre-K students entering Kindergarten, they do **NOT** need to fill in the bubble with a pencil. They will **ONLY** be required to point to the answer.

How to Use These Practice Tests
- Use these practice tests as a diagnostic to see how your child will do on each subtest, or just use it as a full practice test experience.

- This practice test can only be scored on a percentage basis – the total number of correct answers/total questions asked. This assessment is not meant to generate a projected score as it has not been norm-referenced. The goal is to guide you in identifying your child's strengths and weaknesses so that you can work on skills needed for the real test.

The 10 Most Common Test-Taking Mistakes Kids Make

Gently correct your child if you see him or her making one of these mistakes! Also, note these mistakes on the score sheet so you can help your child learn to avoid them. These types of mistakes will cost your child valuable points.

1. **Losing focus**
2. **Not listening carefully**
3. **Not following directions**
4. **Rushing like it's a race**
5. **Not understanding what to do**
6. **Choosing the most obvious answer**
7. **Not considering all answer choices**
8. **Not guessing when they aren't sure**
9. **Getting stuck on a hard question – losing time**
10. **Not eliminating answers they know are wrong before guessing**

How to Administer this Practice Test

- When working through these practice tests, make sure your child is sitting in a quiet and well-lit place where he can focus and do his best.

- Separate the child warm-up questions and child practice questions (pages 21 to 48 for NNAT® and pages 58-68 for OLSAT®) from the rest of the workbook. Staple or clip the pages together. This will be your child's practice test.

- Give your child a short break between the NNAT and OLSAT portions of the practice test.

- Once the practice test starts, don't give your child feedback (i.e. "good job!") or help during the practice test unless he or she is confused about what to do. Go over answers after the test is over.

- Neither of these tests are timed. Although, if your child refuses to answer the questions or stops working during the actual test, the test proctor may stop the test. That's why it's important to have your child build up "test stamina" (the ability to sit still and focus for 45 minutes – 1 hour) before taking the actual test.

- For additional preparation for NNAT and OLSAT, join TestingMom.com where we have thousands more practice questions (plus printables and interactive games) for your child. At the Pre-K to 1st grade level, TestingMom.com's IQ Fun Pack board game is an excellent and fun test prep system to help your child prepare for both NNAT and OLSAT. www.testingmom.com/store.

TestingMom.com ©

WARM-UP QUESTION 1
(Child should be on page 21)

Pattern Completion

The Empty Box = A White Card

Tear out the perforated pages 21 to 48 for the Warm-up Questions and Practice Test in the Child section. Give the Warm-Up Questions to your child first.

Parent, tell your child to imagine that the empty box is a white card covering up part of the pattern. She must find what is underneath! It might help her to look at where the lines and colors in the pattern touch the empty box. When looking at answer choices, she must imagine that the lines and colors are continuing beneath the white card. Have her touch where the lines and colors hit the empty box and then touch the answer choices, looking for those lines and colors to be continued. In the example below, if your child touches where the line hits and then continues "underneath the white card," and looks for an answer choice where the line continues in the same place, it will lead her to C.

Answer: C

| A | B | C | D | E |

Help Your Child Eliminate Wrong Answers
As you read our analysis of these Pattern Completion puzzles, you will see that we often try to immediately eliminate answers that are clearly wrong. Teach your child to do this. That way, if he isn't sure of the answer and has to take a guess, he can improve his odds of getting the question right! Children get 0 points if they miss an answer and 0 points if they skip a question, so it is always worth taking a guess after you've narrowed down your choices. This is also important because by eliminating answers that are wrong, your child learns to look at every answer choice.

Talk Through the Reasoning

Parent, as we go through the examples that follow, we are explaining them to you in words. If your child is very good with visual-spatial reasoning puzzles, he may just "know" the answer without having the words to explain why. If your child "sees" the answer and just "knows" it, that is fine. Most children, however, will benefit from talking their way through the reasoning required to solve each puzzle. When your child is learning how to do these, we encourage you to have him explain his reasoning to you. If he is unsure, you can reason through the puzzle together. When your child is tested, he will be able to talk through his reasoning in his own head.

Practice for Different Reasons - Sometimes Limiting Feedback

Sometimes, work through questions and talk through the reasoning with your child to help her know how to work with this type of question (as described above). Other times, you may want to give your child a series of questions to practice just to see how she does. In those times, limit the amount of feedback you give your child as she works. When a child is tested, the proctor will not tell her if she is right or wrong after each question. As your child works, limit your feedback to comments like, "Nice job working hard," or "You are really trying hard – good job with that," or "Today, you are really paying attention – I like that."

How the Question is Asked

If your child is taking the NNAT, there will be very little explanation within the question about how to solve each one of these puzzles. The question will be asked something like this: "Look at this puzzle. Something is missing in the empty box. Look at these answer choices. Which one belongs in the empty box?"

When you are *teaching* your child how to solve these puzzles, you might ask the question like this, to give your child more direction: **"Look at the pattern. There is a piece missing. Can you see what it is?"** Give your child time to find where the piece is missing.

Then ask, **"Can you point to the answer choice that would complete the pattern if you placed it over the question mark?"**

On page 18, we give you more specific ways to ask the different types of questions for NNAT while your child is still learning. Just remember the question will be asked with very little explanation on the actual test.

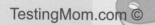

WARM-UP QUESTION 2 (Child should be on page 21) -- Pattern Completion

Parent, say to your child: "Look at the pattern. There is a piece missing. Can you see what it is?" Give your child time to find where the piece is missing.

Then ask, "Can you point to the answer choice that would complete the pattern if you placed it over the question mark?"

Answer: C

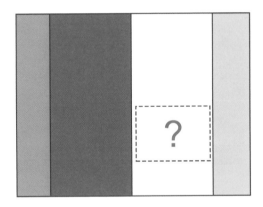

A   B   C   D   E

Parent, help your child see that the empty space covers a part of the picture that is all one color - white. You are looking for a square that is white to fill in that space.
C is the answer.

WARM-UP QUESTION 3 (child should be on page 22) -- Pattern Completion

Parent, say to your child: "Look at the pattern. There is a piece missing. Can you see what it is?" Give your child time to find where the piece is missing.

Then ask, "Can you point to the answer choice that would complete the pattern if you placed it over the question mark?"

Answer: D

Parent, help your child see that the empty space covers a part of the picture that is a blue line drawing with yellow outside of the lower right corner of the inside rectangle. There is also some white being covered up by the empty space. D is the answer.

WARM-UP QUESTION 4 (Child should be on page 22) -- Reasoning by Analogy

What's the relationship on top? Help your child see the relationship between the 2 items on top - they are the same shape and same color.

What figure are we "matching?" On the bottom row, we see a green circle.

What relationship are we trying to "match?" We are looking for an answer that is the same shape and color as the green circle on the bottom row. That way, the shapes on the bottom will have the same relationship to each other as the shapes on top.

Which answers are clearly wrong? The A, B, C, E can be eliminated. A, B and E are circles, but they aren't the same color. C is the same color, but it isn't a circle.

Parent, say to your child: "Look at the figures on top. They go together in some way. Choose a figure from the answer row that goes with the figure on the bottom the same way the figures on top go together."

Answer: D

A	B	C	D	E

WARM-UP QUESTION 5 (Child should be on page 23) – Serial Reasoning

Parent, say to your child: "Look at the shapes across the rows and up and down the columns. There is a pattern. Do you see what it is?" Give your child some time to see if she can recognize the pattern.

Then say to your child, "Can you find the answer in the bottom row that belongs in the empty box so that the pattern inside the rows and columns will be complete?"

Parent, help your child see that the diamonds alternate from white to blue across the 9 boxes. Another way to look at this is, the corners and the middle diamonds are white and the diamonds in between are blue. D is the correct answer.

In order to help your child learn to eliminate answers that are clearly wrong, have her explain to you why all the answers other than D are wrong.

Answer: D

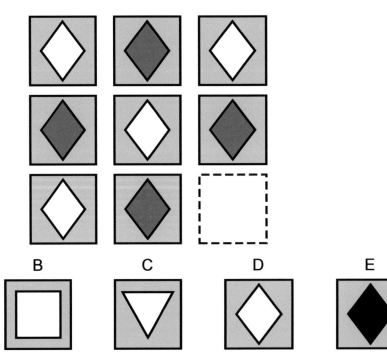

WARM-UP QUESTION 6 (Child should be on page 23)
Spatial Visualization -- Combination

Spatial Visualization, as you can imagine, tests spatial reasoning skills. In these questions, children must envision how objects might look when folded, rotated, or otherwise combined. In combination-type questions, the child is shown three boxes across the top. The first two boxes combine to make the design in the third box. The child must choose the answer that shows what the last box would look like if the first two boxes on the bottom were combined the same way the top boxes were combined.

These questions are designed to test one thing: how well your child can rearrange shapes and images inside of his head. Because of this, the most important and useful thing you can do for your child is to practice these types of questions and build the visual-spatial reasoning abilities needed to solve them.

Parent, tell your child this for a Combination question: "Look at the pictures on top. If you combine the first two, it would look like the third picture. Now look at the pictures in the second row. If you combined them the way the pictures on top were combined, it will look like one of the answer choices. Can you find the answer that shows what the two pictures in the second row will look like after they are combined?"

Parent, help your child see this: When you combine the yellow and green figures, the yellow will be on the right and the green on the left. This eliminates answers C and D. Since the jagged line is at an angle in the two pieces, B is the only possible answer.

Answer: B

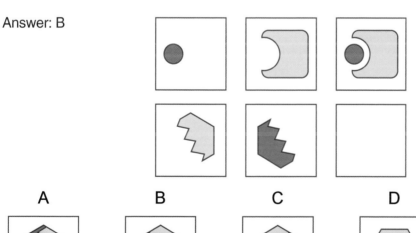

   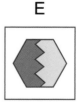

A   B   C   D   E

WARM-UP QUESTION 7 (Child should be on page 24)
Spatial Visualization – Folding Tabs

Parent, ask your child this for a Folding Tab question: "Look at the pictures on top. When the outside piece is folded in, it will look like the picture on the right. Now look at the picture on the second row. Choose the answer from the bottom that shows what the picture will look like if the outside piece is folded in like the pictures on top."

Parent, help your child see this: When that gold triangle on top gets folded in, there will be a small triangle on the top of the blue box pointing down. There are only 2 answers with gold triangles on top pointing down – A and C. The triangle in the A answer is too big. C is the only possible answer.

Answer: C

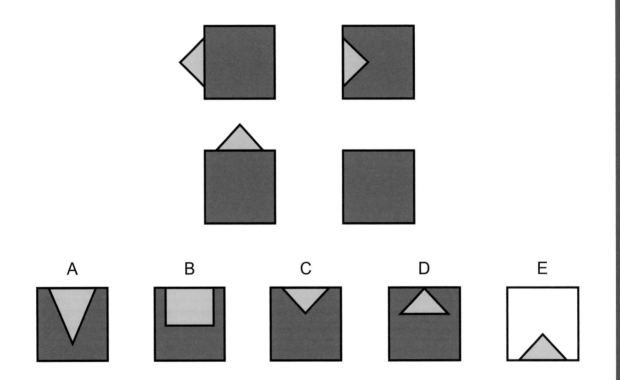

STOP

Remove this Answer and Score Sheet Pages 17-20. Fill it out as your child answers questions.

Answer and Score Sheet For Practice Test For NNAT® – Parent Section

Answer and Score Sheet for Practice Test for NNAT

Question	Answer	Child's Answer	Question Type	Question	Answer	Child's Answer	Question Type
1	B		Pattern Completion	25	B		Serial Reasoning
2	D		Pattern Completion	26	C		Serial Reasoning
3	C		Reasoning by Analogy	27	B		Reasoning by Analogy
4	D		Reasoning by Analogy	28	C		Reasoning by Analogy
5	C		Serial Reasoning	29	B		Reasoning by Analogy
6	E		Serial Reasoning	30	D		Serial Reasoning
7	C		Pattern Completion	31	A		Serial Reasoning
8	B		Reasoning by Analogy	32	C		Pattern Completion
9	A		Reasoning by Analogy	33	A		Spatial Visualization
10	A		Pattern Completion	34	D		Pattern Completion
11	B		Serial Reasoning	35	A		Reasoning by Analogy
12	E		Serial Reasoning	36	E		Reasoning by Analogy
13	B		Reasoning by Analogy	37	E		Spatial Visualization
14	B		Reasoning by Analogy	38	B		Reasoning by Analogy
15	C		Reasoning by Analogy	39	B		Reasoning by Analogy
16	D		Spatial Visualization	40	D		Pattern Completion
17	C		Pattern Completion	41	E		Pattern Completion
18	C		Pattern Completion	42	E		Pattern Completion
19	D		Reasoning by Analogy	43	C		Reasoning by Analogy
20	B		Reasoning by Analogy	44	A		Reasoning by Analogy
21	B		Serial Reasoning	45	D		Reasoning by Analogy
22	E		Serial Reasoning	46	C		Serial Reasoning
23	E		Pattern Completion	47	E		Pattern Completion
24	B		Pattern Completion	48	C		Serial Reasoning

Parent's Notes:

_____

_____

_____

_____

Mastery Level of Skill

Question Type:	Number Correct	# of Questions	Development Needed	Demonstrates Skill	Proficient Skill
Pattern Completion		14	0 to 5	6 to 10	11 to 14
Reasoning by Analogy		19	0 to 5	6 to 12	13 to 19
Serial Reasoning		12	0 to 4	5 to 8	9 to 12
Spatial Visualization		3	0 to 1	2	3

Here's how to ask the questions when your child is learning:

All Pattern Completion Questions
Parent, tell your child this: "Look at the pattern on top. A piece has been taken out of it. Choose the piece from the answer row that goes where the question mark is in order to complete the pattern."

All Reasoning By Analogy Questions
Parent, tell your child this: "Look at the figures on top. They go together in a certain way. Choose the figure from the answer row that goes in the empty space because it belongs with the figure(s) on the bottom the same way the figures on top belong together."

All Serial Reasoning Questions
Parent, tell your child this: "Look at the shapes in the boxes across the rows and up and down the columns. Do you see how they are related to each other? Can you find the answer that goes in the empty box so the pattern inside the rows and columns will be complete."

All Spatial Visualization Questions
Type 1 (Combination) Parent, tell your child this: "Look at the pictures on top. If you combine the first two, it would look like the third picture. Now look at the pictures in the second row. If you combined them the way the pictures on top were combined, it will look like one of the answer choices. Can you find the answer that shows what the two pictures in the second row will look like after they are combined?"

Type 2 (Folding Tabs) Parent, tell your child this: "Look at the pictures on top. When the outside pieces are folded in, it will look like the picture on the top right. Look at the picture in the second row. Choose the answer from the bottom that shows what it will look like if the outside pieces are folded in just like the pictures on top."

During the Actual Test

After your child has gone through some warm-up sample questions, he will be told to work through the test at his own pace. "Now you complete the rest of the puzzles. Which one of the answer pictures should go in the empty box?"

Answers with Explanations

1. B   (Pattern Completion)

2. D   (Pattern Completion)

3. C   – top has blue box in inside corner top, bottom has blue box in inside corner bottom (Reasoning by Analogy)

4. D   – second box design is half of first box design (Reasoning by Analogy)

5. C   – each row and column has one of each shape and color (Serial Reasoning)

6. E   – each row and column has a small, medium and large gold circle (Serial Reasoning)

7. C   (Pattern Completion)

8. B   – turn 90 degrees clockwise (Reasoning by Analogy)

9. A   – final box makes an overall design – like a puzzle piece (Reasoning by Analogy)

10. A   (Pattern Completion)

11. B   – each row and column has one of each shape and color, missing a starburst shape and a gold color (Serial Reasoning)

12. E   – each row and column has a solid heart and a heart split on the top and the bottom (Serial Reasoning)

13. B   – designs have same number of sides (Reasoning by Analogy)

14. B   – all boxes have a single line, same width (Reasoning by Analogy)

15. C   – opposite (Reasoning by Analogy)

16. D   (Spatial Visualization)

17. C   (Pattern Completion)

18. C   (Pattern Completion)

19. D   – pink line covers a new side with each box (Reasoning by Analogy)

20. B   – 4th box is analogous to first top box, but opposite (Reasoning by Analogy)

21. B   – green moves one over in each row – 2 pinks in each row and column (Serial Reasoning)

22. E   – blue keeps alternating sides of the oval (Serial Reasoning)

23. E (Pattern Completion)
24. B (Pattern Completion)
25. B – each row and column has one of each shape and size; missing a medium sized diamond (Serial Reasoning)
26. C – each row and column has one of each shape and color (Serial Reasoning)
27. B – first and last box of each row is same color. (Reasoning by Analogy)
28. C – each second box in a row adds one color from the first box in that row (Reasoning by Analogy)
29. B – the two outside colors change places; the middle white color and the design remain the same (Reasoning by Analogy)
30. D – alternating pentagon – star pattern (Serial Reasoning)
31. A – shape alternates between pointing up and pointing sideways (Serial Reasoning)
32. C (Pattern Completion)
33. A (Spatial Visualization)
34. D (Pattern Completion)
35. A (Reasoning by Analogy)
36. E – each design is pink and yellow (Reasoning by Analogy)
37. E – first and second boxes combine to make third box (Spatial Visualization)
38. B – each design is pink and blue (Reasoning by Analogy)
39. B – design on right has one more element than design on left – designs on right are all intersecting circles (Reasoning by Analogy)
40. D (Pattern Completion)
41. E (Pattern Completion)
42. E – each star has one fewer point (Pattern Completion)
43. C – final box makes an overall design – like a puzzle piece (Reasoning by Analogy)
44. A – design on right is always a vertical version of design on left   (Reasoning by Analogy)
45. D – same design but opposite colors (Reasoning by Analogy)
46. C – the white dot is in one of three positions inside the green circles across the rows and up and down the columns (Serial Reasoning)
47. E (Pattern Completion)
48. C – each row and column has one of each shape and color; missing a heart and a gold star (Serial Reasoning)

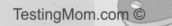

WARM-UP
1.

STOP

Remove pages 21 to 48 and give to child.

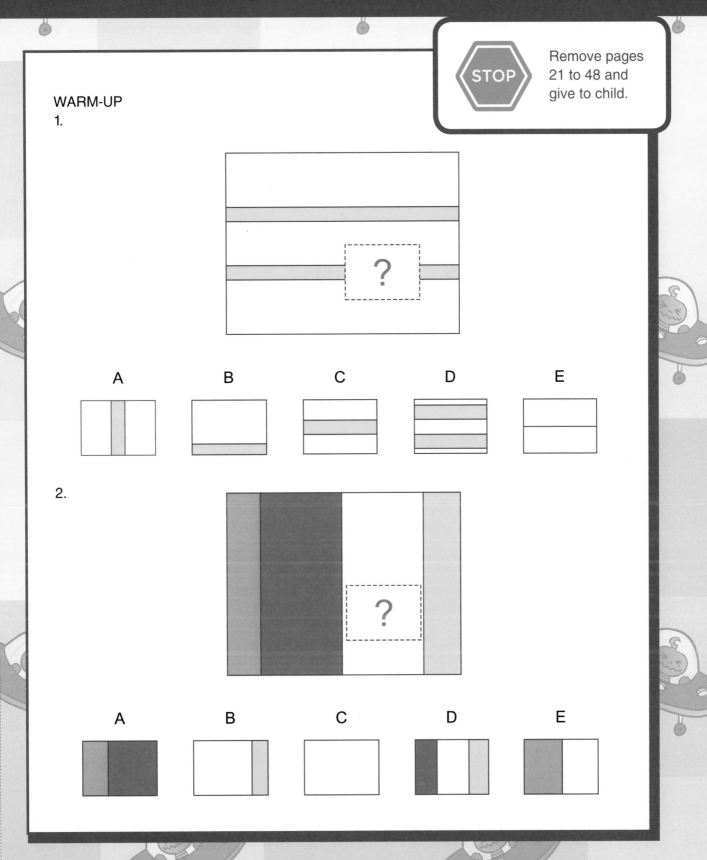

2.

WARM-UP
3.

A   B   C   D   E

4.

A   B   C   D   E

WARM-UP
5.

A	B	C	D	E

6.

A	B	C	D	E

WARM-UP
7

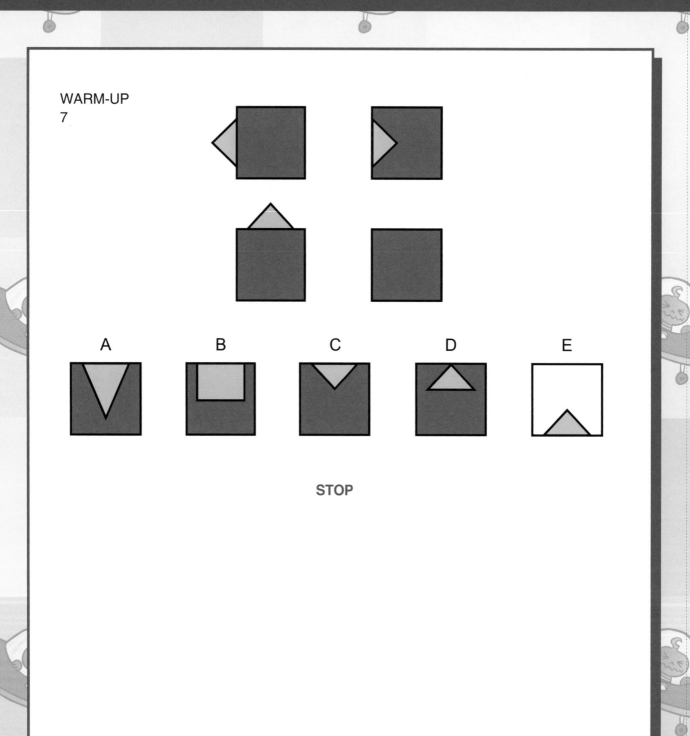

STOP

1.

A	B	C	D	E

2.

A	B	C	D	E

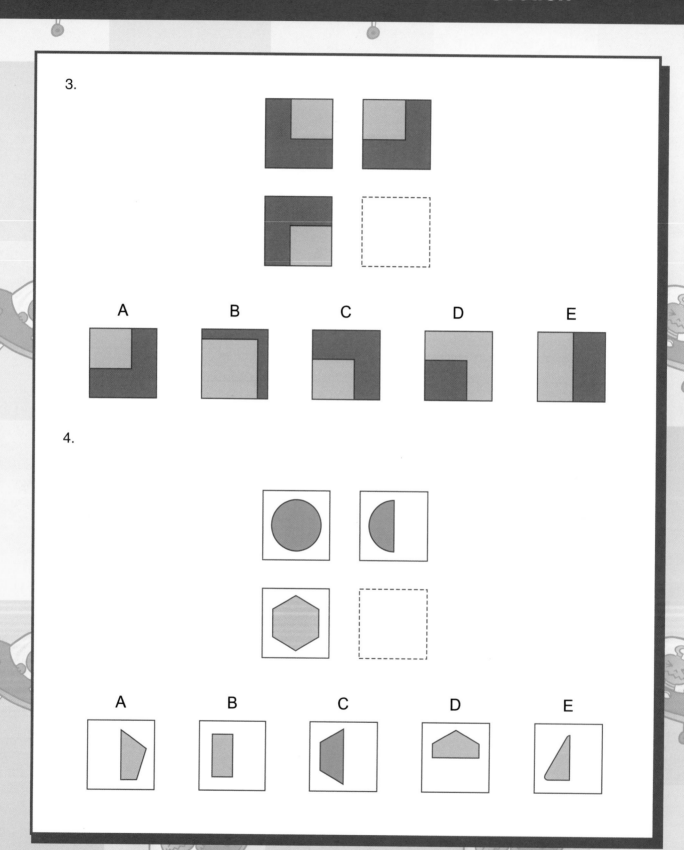

3.

4.

5.

6.

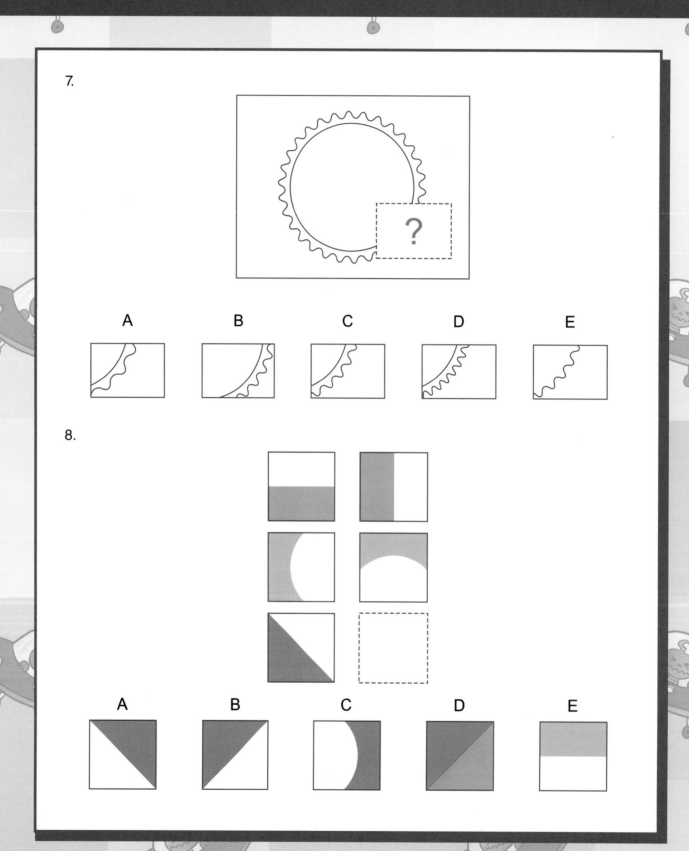

7.

8.

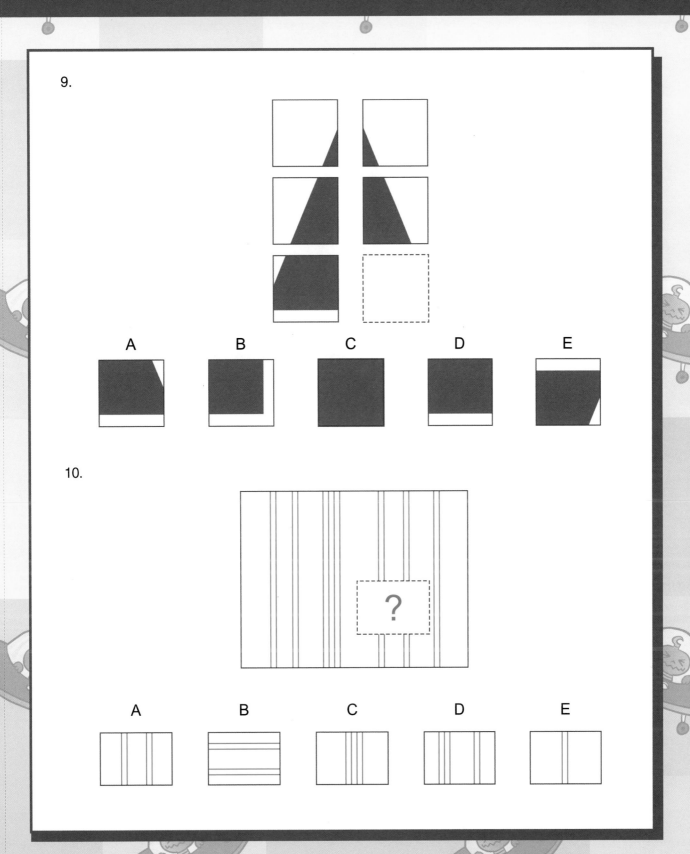

9.

10.

11.

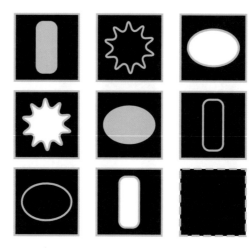

A	B	C	D	E

12.

A	B	C	D	E

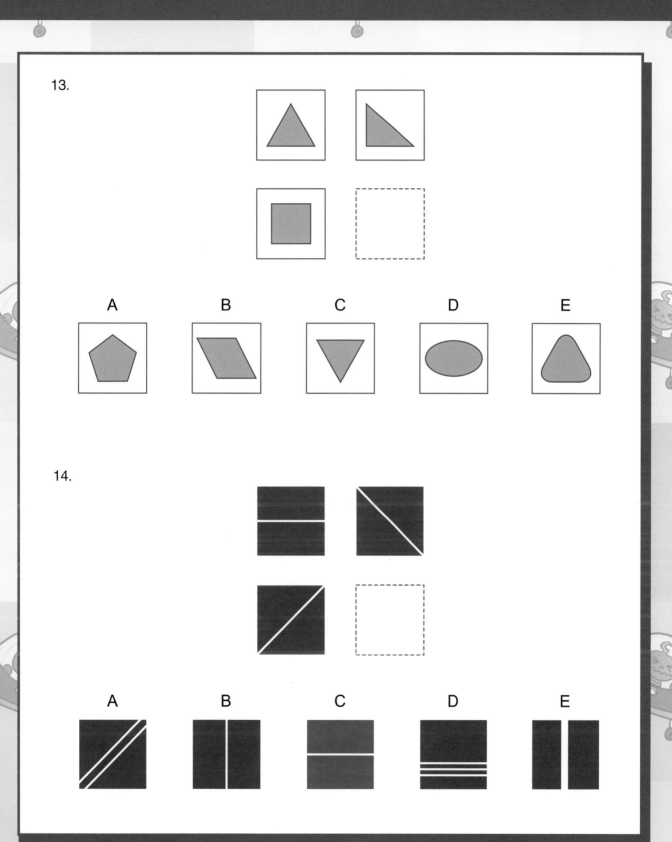

13.

14.

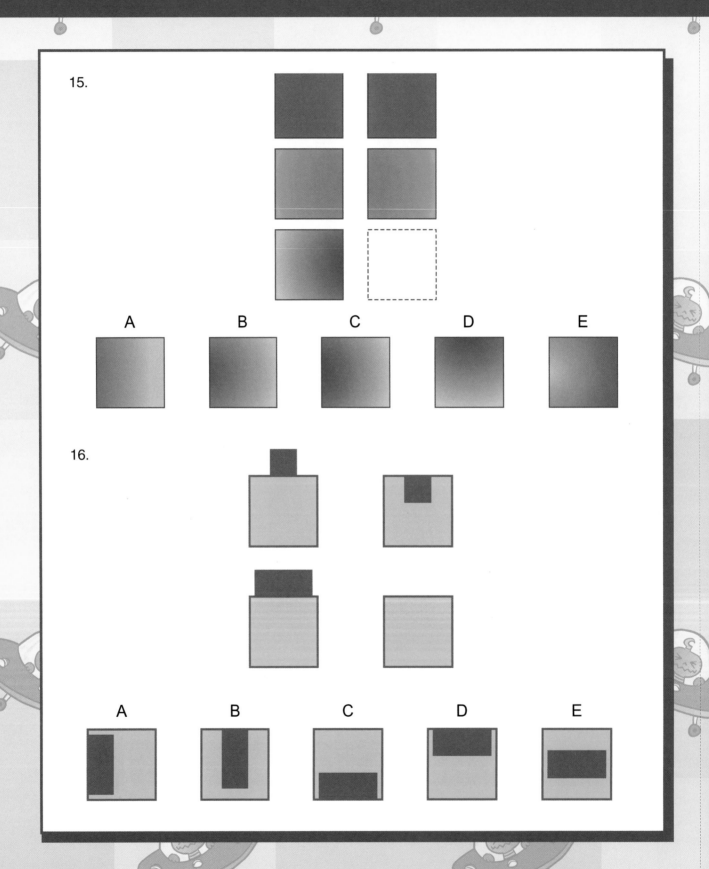

15.

A   B   C   D   E

16.

A   B   C   D   E

17.

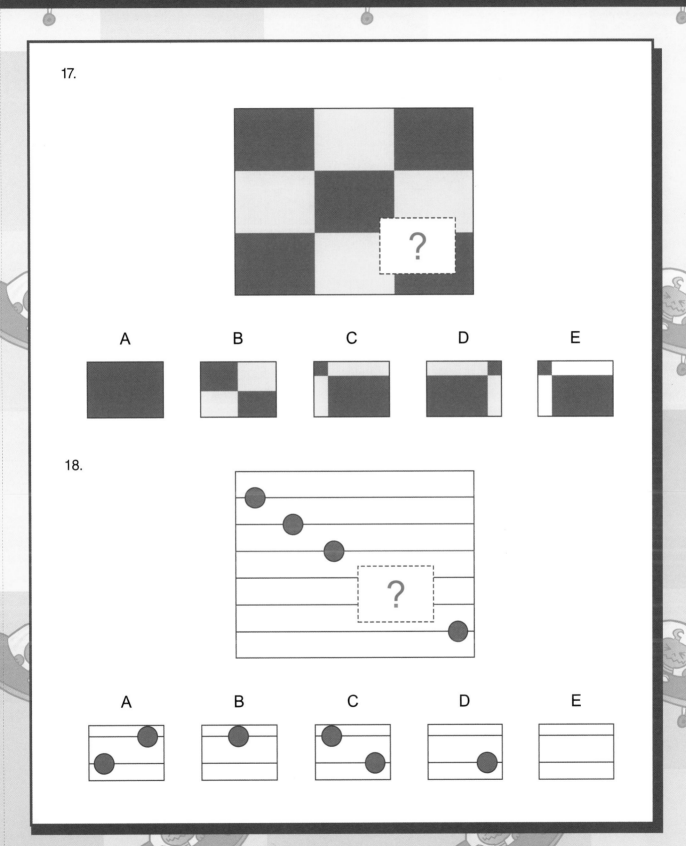

A   B   C   D   E

18.

A   B   C   D   E

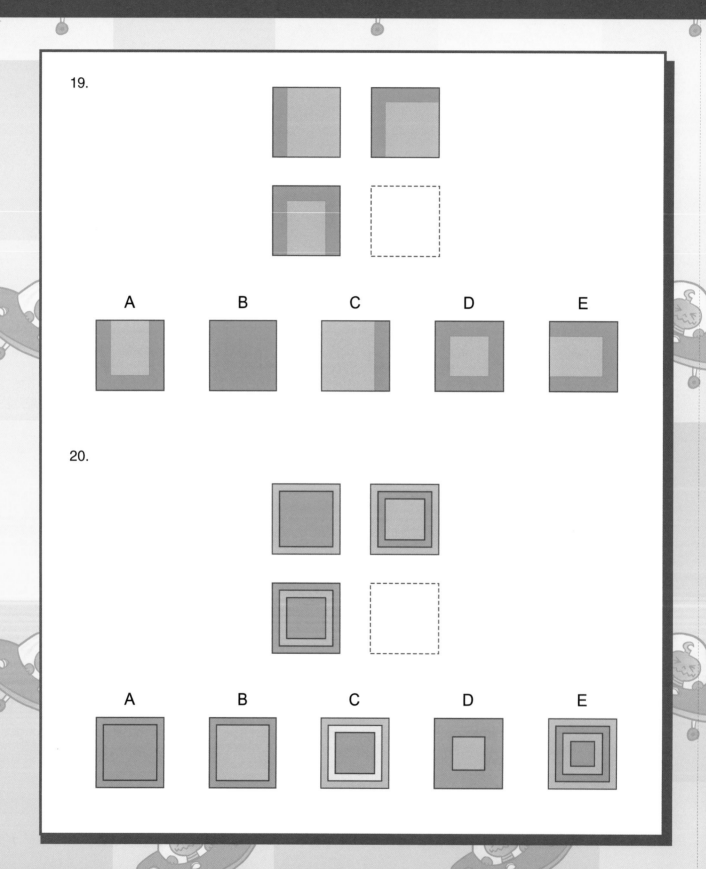

19.

20.

21.

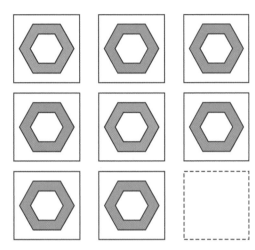

A	B	C	D	E

22.

A	B	C	D	E

23.

A B C D E

24.

A B C D E

25.

A	B	C	D	E

26.

A	B	C	D	E

27.

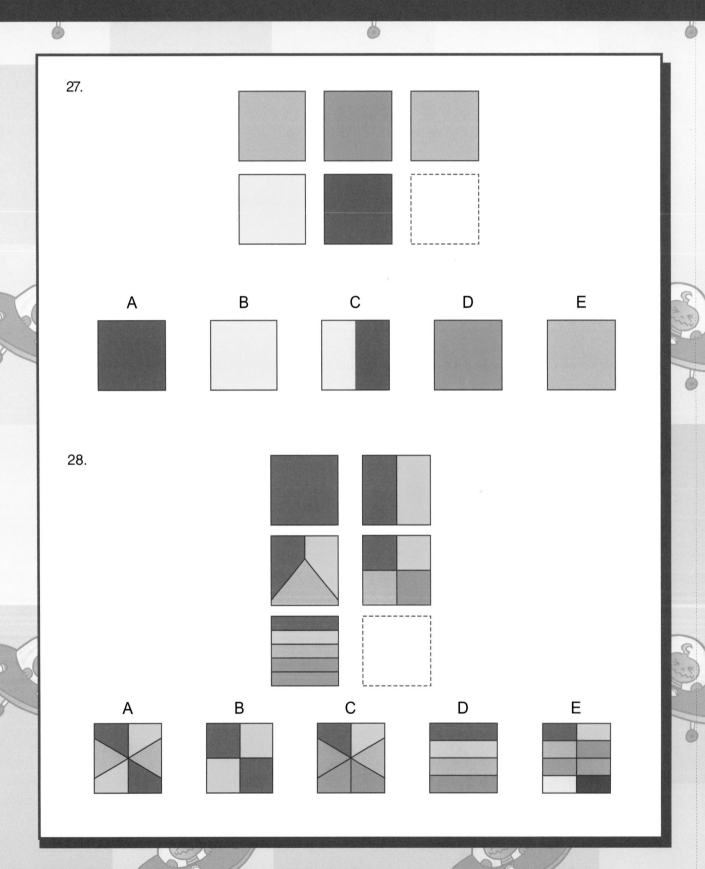

28.

29.

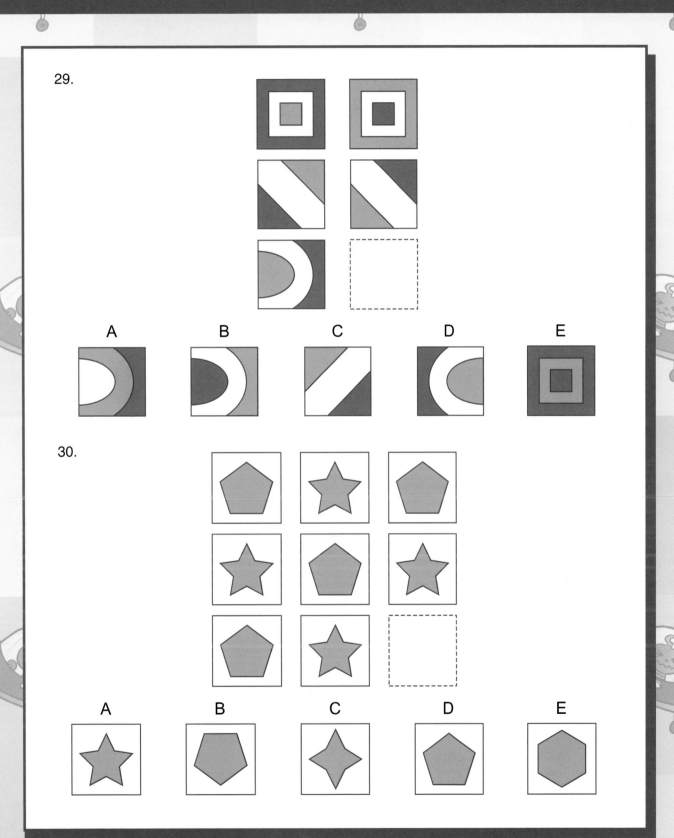

30.

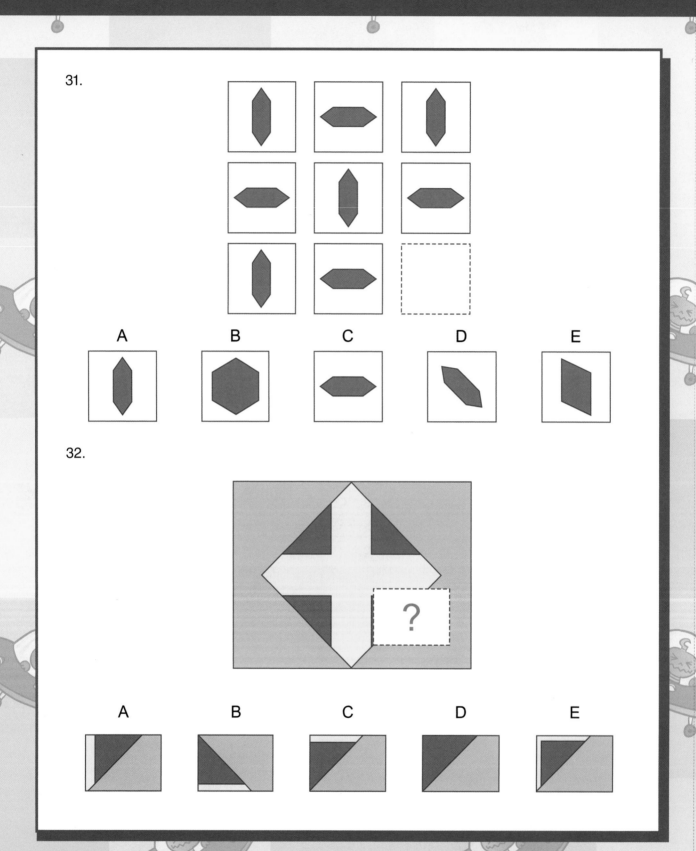

31.

A   B   C   D   E

32.

A   B   C   D   E

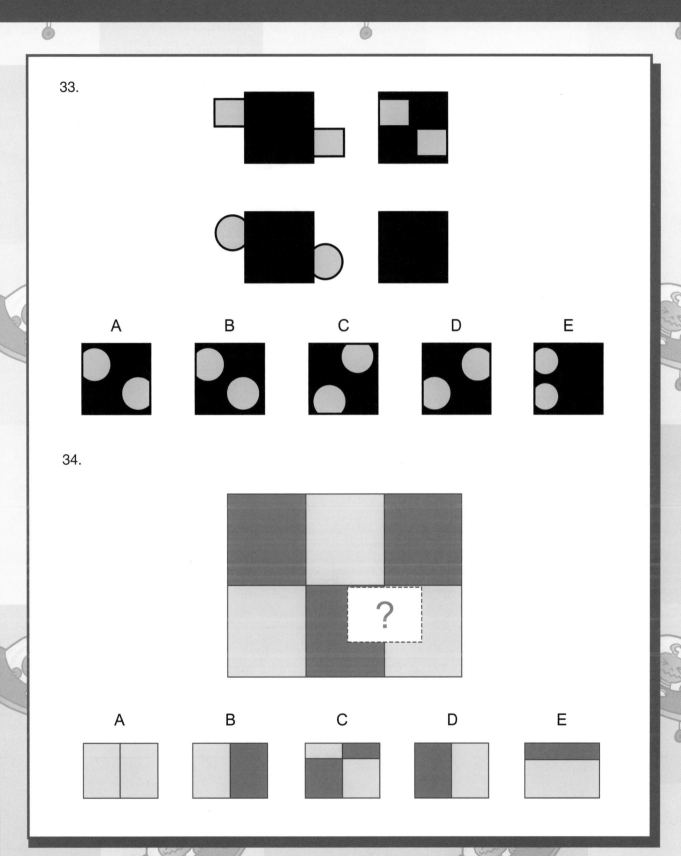

33.

A   B   C   D   E

34.

A   B   C   D   E

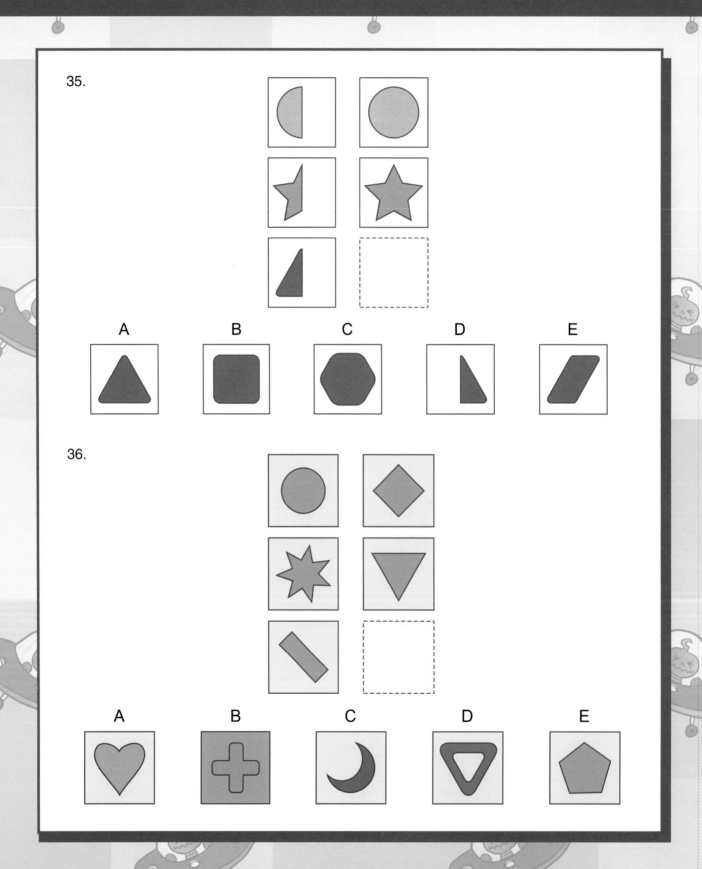

35.

A   B   C   D   E

36.

A   B   C   D   E

37.

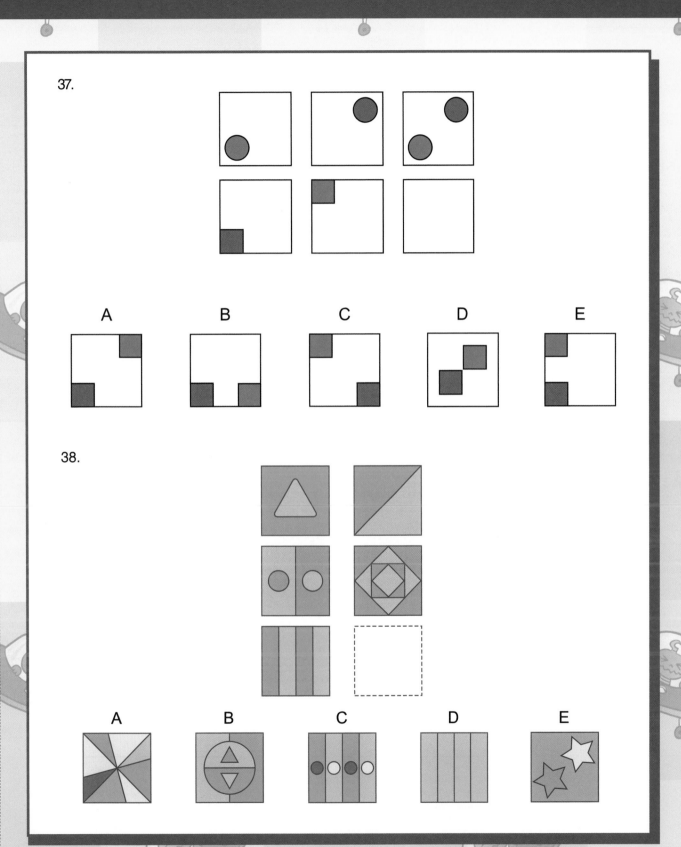

A   B   C   D   E

38.

A   B   C   D   E

39.

A B C D E

40.

A B C D E

41.

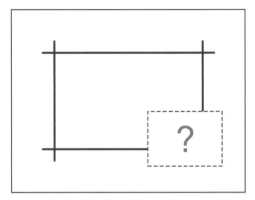

A	B	C	D	E

42.

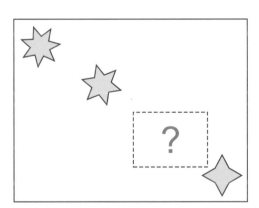

A	B	C	D	E

43.

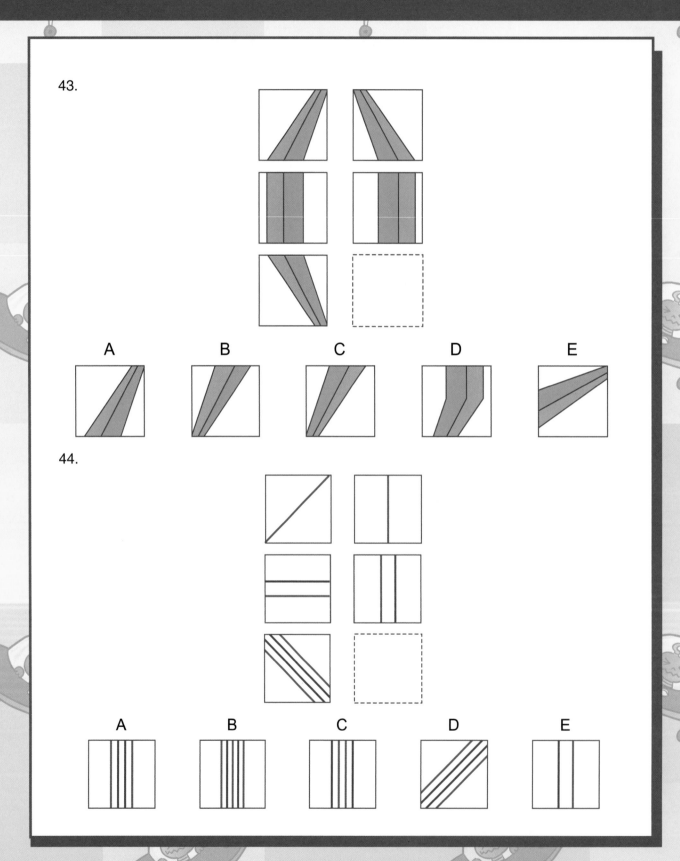

44.

45.

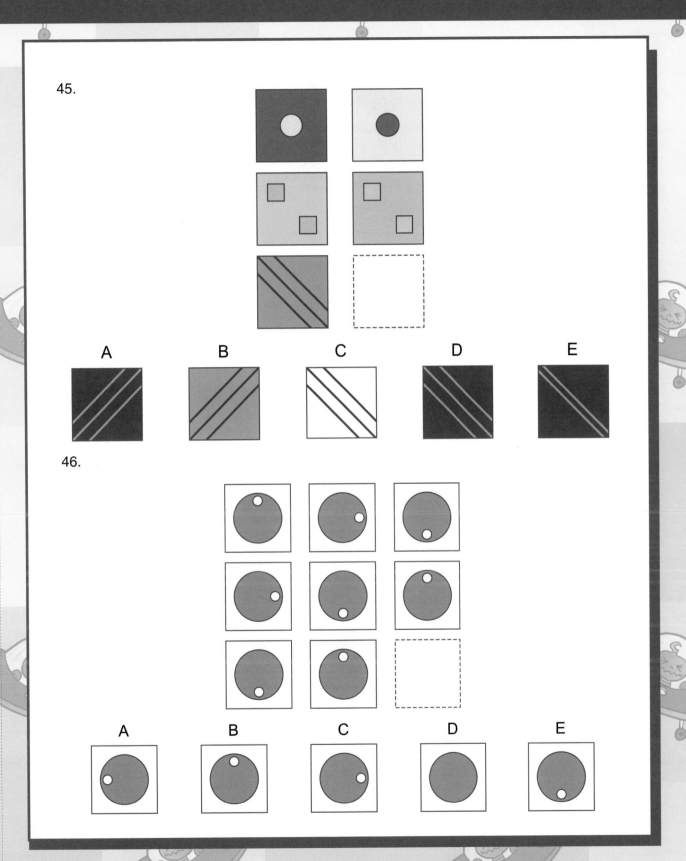

46.

47.

A	B	C	D	E

48.

A	B	C	D	E

Tear out pages 59 to 69 for your child's Warm-up questions and Practical Test. Give the Warm-Up questions to your child first.

Note: If your child is in kindergarten going into first grade he or she will be required to fill out the bubble under the correct answer. When reading the questions aloud, please substitute the word "Mark" for the words "Point to".

WARM-UP QUESTION 1 — Aural Reasoning
Child should be on page 59

The types of questions that you'll find most often under Aural Reasoning are questions that require children to use reasoning skills to:

1. Identify similarities and differences between objects,
2. Identify spatial, temporal, or logical relationships of objects (prepositions),
3. Demonstrate an understanding of vocabulary words, or
4. Visualize a situation based on verbal description, integrate the details, pull together the relevant information, and choose the picture that answers the question.

Parent, say to your child: "Put your finger on the row where you see the tiny lion. Here is a question about the pictures in that row. Julie planted some seeds in her garden. She watered them every day. After one week three of the seeds grew into flowers. Point to the picture that shows Julie's garden." **Answer: 1st image over the bubble**

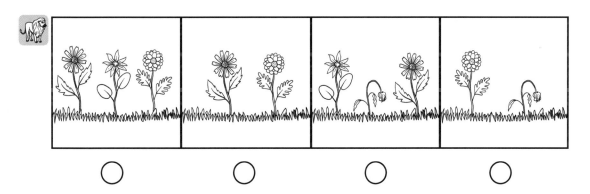

Parent: Help your child see that the first picture is the only one that shows three seeds that have grown into flowers. That can be the only answer.

WARM-UP QUESTION 2 — Following Directions
Child should be on page 59

The types of questions that you'll find most often under Following Directions are questions that require children to use listening and remembering skills to:
1. Identify similarities and differences between objects,
2. Identify spatial, temporal, or logical relationships of objects (prepositions),
3. Demonstrate an understanding of quantitative concepts,
4. Demonstrate an understanding of comparative position or sequence/rank, or
5. Select a picture that corresponds to a verbal description that is read out loud.

Parent, say to your child: "Put your finger on the row where you see the tiny sugar bowl. Here is a question about the pictures in that row. Point to the picture that does not have a drink."
Answer: 1st image over the bubble

Parent, say to your child: Help your child see that the second, third, and fourth pictures all show a picture of a drink. The first picture can be the only answer.

WARM-UP QUESTION 3 — Arithmetic Reasoning
Child should be on page 59

The types of questions that you'll find most often under Arithmetic Reasoning are verbal story problems that are solved through basic math skills. Students must be able to:

1. Count,
2. Do basic addition and subtraction,
3. Demonstrate knowledge of relativity (more, less, fewer, bigger, smaller, same, equal, etc.),
4. Demonstrate knowledge of math vocabulary (dozen, pair, etc.),
5. Demonstrate knowledge of basic division and multiplication through concepts such as half as much, twice as many, divide something evenly.

Parent, say to your child: Put your finger on the row where you see the tiny glass. Jake's mom gave him pencils you see at the beginning of the row. Jake sharpened two of the pencils evenly and brought them to school. Point to the picture that shows the pencils Jake brought to school.
Answer: 2nd image over the bubble

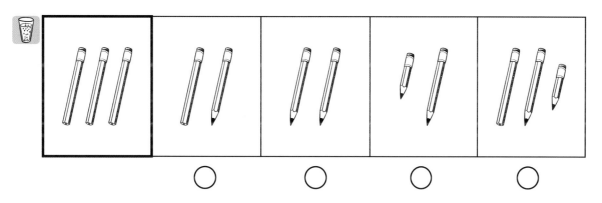

Parent: Help your child to see that only the second picture over the bubble shows a picture of two pencils that have been evenly sharpened. That can be the only answer. In order to help your child learn how to eliminate answers that are clearly wrong, have him explain to you why the answers other than the second one are incorrect.

Child should be on page 60

Note: If your child is applying to kindergarten have her point to the answer. If your child is applying to first grade substitute the word "Mark" for the words "Point to" and have your child fill in the bubble under the correct answer.

1. Put your finger on the row where you see the tiny cup. Here is a question about the pictures in that row. For Dana's art project, she used five things. Three of the things were the same. Point to the picture that shows what Dana used for her art project. **Answer: 4th image over the bubble**

2. Put your finger on the row where you see the tiny planet. Here is a question about the pictures in that row. James and Ben went apple picking. They picked the same amount of apples and put them in their own baskets. Point to the picture that shows James and Ben's apple baskets.
Answer: 2nd image over the bubble

3. Put your finger on the row where you see the tiny violin. Here is a question about the pictures in that row. Point to the picture with two trees.
Answer: 2nd image over the bubble

4. Put your finger on the row where you see the tiny faucet. Here is a question about the pictures in that row. Point to the picture that shows two cats sitting on the ground and a black cat on the fence.
Answer: 3rd image over the bubble

5. Put your finger on the row where you see the tiny racquet. Lila went to the zoo and saw the number of penguins you see at the beginning of the row. She also saw two less alligators than penguins. Point to the picture that shows how many alligators Lila saw at the zoo.
Answer: 3rd image over the bubble

6. Put your finger on the row where you see the tiny tractor. At the beginning of the row, you see flowers in a garden. Carla picked one flower for her mom and three flowers for her grandma. Point to the picture that shows how many flowers were left in the garden.
Answer: 3rd image over the bubble

7. Put your finger on the row where you see the tiny shell. Here is a question about the pictures in that row. Jill's teacher said to draw your favorite zoo animals. When you are done, write your name on the top of the paper. Point to the picture that shows Jill's drawing if she followed her teacher's directions.
Answer: 2nd image over the bubble (the first picture is one animal and the third and fourth pictures are farm animals)

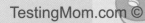

8. Put your finger on the row where you see the tiny shoe. Here is a question about the pictures in that row. Sidney wants to play on something at the park. After she climbs to the top, she can crawl across to the other side. Point to the picture that shows what Sidney wants to play on at the park.
Answer: 4th image over the bubble

9. Put your finger on the row where you see the tiny airplane. Here is a question about the pictures in that row. Point to the letter above the number 3.
Answer: 3rd row, 4th column (R)

10. Put your finger on the row where you see the tiny cube. Here is a question about the pictures in that row. Point to the picture that shows the row of fruit where the last fruit is a banana.
Answer: 2nd image over the bubble

11. Put your finger on the row where you see the tiny trophy. Gabby's mom gave her 5 strawberries for dessert. Point to the picture that shows how many strawberries Gabby's mom gave her for dessert.
Answer: 4th image over the bubble

12. Put your finger on the row where you see the tiny ball of yarn. James, John and Joe spent the day at the beach collecting shells. They each found two shells to keep. Point to the picture that shows how many shells James, John and Joe collected altogether. **Answer: 1st image over the bubble**

13. Put your finger on the row where you see the tiny cup. Here is a question about the pictures in that row. Alyse and her brother Luis were playing football in the park. Alyse said "Throw me the ball." Point to the picture that shows Alyse and Luis playing in the park.
Answer: 2nd image over the bubble

14. Put your finger on the row where you see the tiny sock. Here is a question about the pictures in that row. Jo had some oranges. She peeled two. She ate part of one orange and all of the other. Point to the picture that shows what Jo had left over.
Answer: 4th image over the bubble

15. Put your finger on the row where you see the tiny gingerbread man. Here is a question about the pictures in that row. Point to the picture that shows two circles in the same row.
Answer: 3rd image over the bubble

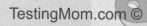

16. Put your finger on the row where you see the tiny harp. Here is a question about the pictures in that row. Point to the picture that shows two triangles to the side of the square.
Answer: 3rd image over the bubble

17. Put your finger on the row where you see the tiny tug boat. Brian drinks 8 glasses of water each day. Brian already drank 4 glasses of water today. Point to the picture that shows how many glasses of water Brian already drank.
Answer: 1st image over the bubble

18. Put your finger on the row where you see the tiny chair. Amy, Jen, Sam and Lisa each had two cookies. Point to the picture that show how many cookies Amy, Jen, Sam and Lisa had altogether.
Answer: 2nd image over the bubble

19. Put your finger on the row where you see the tiny bat. Here is a question about the pictures in that row. Suzie went to the store to buy fruit. She picked out five pieces of fruit. Two were the same and three were different. Point to the picture that shows the fruit Suzie bought at the store.
Answer: 2nd image over the bubble

20. Put your finger on the row where you see the tiny cookie. Here is a question about the pictures in that row. Sally and her family were going on vacation to the ski slopes. Point to the picture that shows what Sally might have packed for her family vacation to the ski slopes.
Answer: 1st image over the bubble

21. Put your finger on the row where you see the tiny skate. Here is a question about the pictures in that row. Point to the picture that shows two swing sets.
Answer: 4th image over the bubble

22. Put your finger on the row where you see the tiny football. Here is a question about the pictures in that row. Point to the picture that shows two people outside the pool.
Answer: 4th image over the bubble

23. Put your finger on the row where you see the tiny cat. Joyce collected the stamps you see at the beginning of the row. Brooke had half as many stamps in her collection as Joyce. Point to the picture that shows Brooke's stamp collection.
Answer: 3rd image over the bubble

24. Put your finger on the row where you see the tiny flower. Larry has the number of pennies you see at the beginning of the row. He then lost three pennies. Point to the picture that shows how many pennies Larry has now.
Answer: 4th image over the bubble

25. Put your finger on the row where you see the tiny crab. Here is a question about the pictures in that row. Evan's socks came back from the laundry. Three were left without any matches. Point to that picture that shows the socks Evan got back from the laundry.
Answer: 3rd image over the bubble

26. Put your finger on the row where you see the tiny cap. Here is a question about the pictures in that row. Chris is an athlete and likes to play sports. The ball for his favorite sport is not round. Point to the picture that shows the ball for Chris' favorite sport.
Answer: 2nd image over the bubble

27. Put your finger on the row where you see the tiny paper airplane. Here is a question about the pictures in that row. Point to the thing in the first row, third column.
Answer: 1st row, 3rd column (circle)

28. Put your finger on the row where you see the tiny doll. Here is a question about the pictures in that row. Point to the picture that shows two squares next to each other.
Answer: 2nd image over the bubble

29. Put your finger on the row where you see the tiny soccer ball. Jenna saw the number of butterflies you see at the beginning of the row at the park. Three of the butterflies flew away. Point to the picture that shows how many butterflies were left.
Answer: 4th image over the bubble

30. Put your finger on the row where you see the tiny shoe. Tracy had the number of balloons you see at the beginning of the row. Four balloons popped. Point to the picture that shows how many balloons Tracy had left.
Answer: 3rd image over the bubble

Answer and Score Sheet For Practice Test For OLSAT® – Parent Section

 STOP Remove pages 56-57 and fill it out as your child answers the questions.

Answer and Score Sheet – Practice Test for OLSAT Verbal Portion

Question	Child's Answer	Answer and Question Type
1		4th image - Aural Reasoning
2		2nd image - Aural Reasoning
3		2nd image - Following Directions
4		3rd image - Following Directions
5		3rd image - Arithmetic Reasoning
6		3rd image - Arithmetic Reasoning
7		2nd image - Aural Reasoning
8		4th image - Aural Reasoning
9		3rd row, 4th column - Following Directions
10		2nd image - Following Directions
11		4th image - Arithmetic Reasoning
12		1st image - Arithmetic Reasoning
13		2nd image - Aural Reasoning
14		4th image - Aural Reasoning
15		3rd image - Following Directions
16		3rd image - Following Directions

17		1st image - Arithmetic Reasoning
18		2nd image - Arithmetic Reasoning
19		2nd image - Aural Reasoning
20		1st image - Aural Reasoning
21		4th image - Following Directions
22		4th image - Following Directions
23		3rd image - Arithmetic Reasoning
24		4th image - Arithmetic Reasoning
25		3rd image - Aural Reasoning
26		2nd image - Aural Reasoning
27		1st row, 3rd column - Following Directions
28		2nd image - Following Directions
29		4th image - Arithmetic Reasoning
30		3rd image - Arithmetic Reasoning

Question Type:	Number Correct	# of Questions	Development Needed	Demonstrates Skill	Proficient Skill
Aural Reasoning		10	0 to 4	5 to 7	8 to 10
Following Directions		10	0 to 4	5 to 7	8 to 10
Arithmetic Reasoning		10	0 to 4	5 to 7	8 to 10

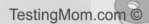

Remove pages 59 to 69 and give to child.

Warm-up 1

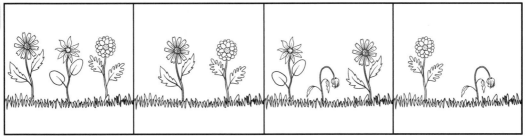

○   ○   ○   ○

Warm-up 2

○   ○   ○   ○

Warm-up 3

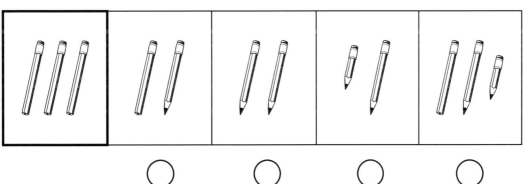

○   ○   ○   ○

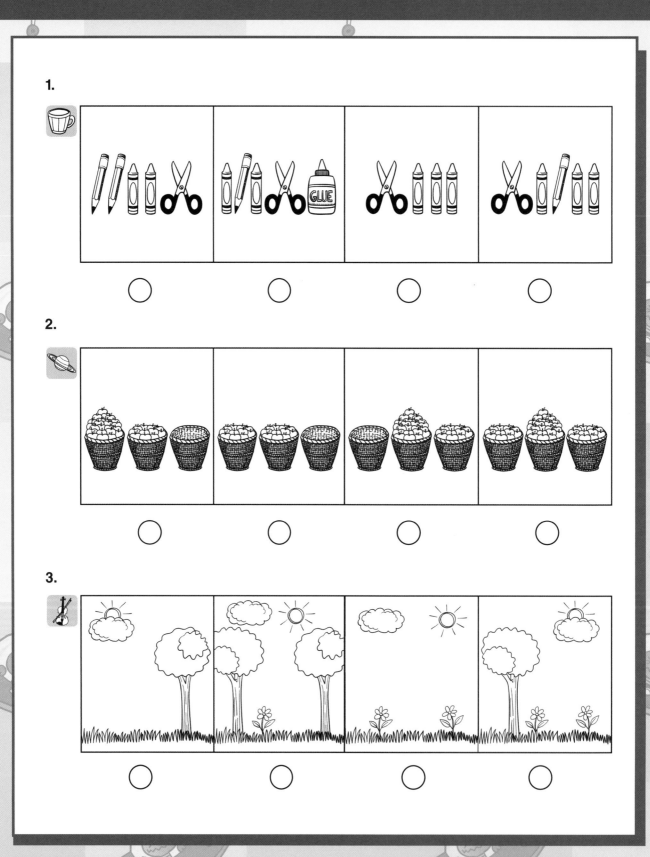

1.

2.

3.

4.

◯   ◯   ◯   ◯

5.

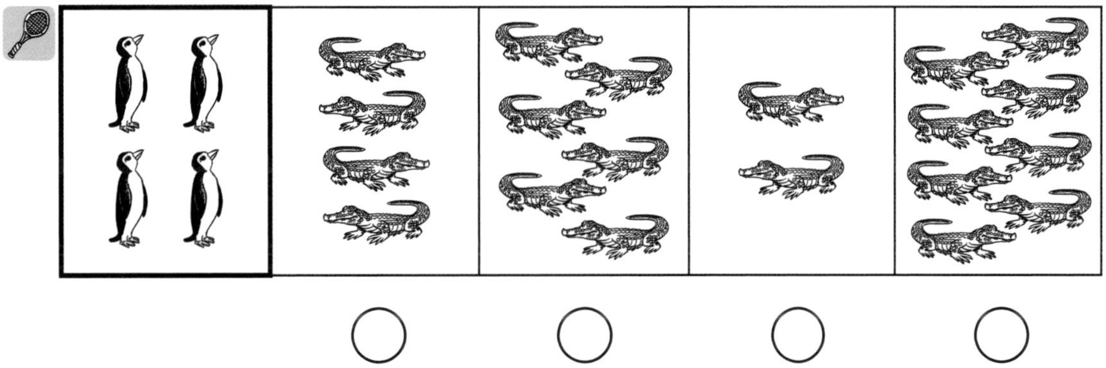

◯   ◯   ◯   ◯

6.

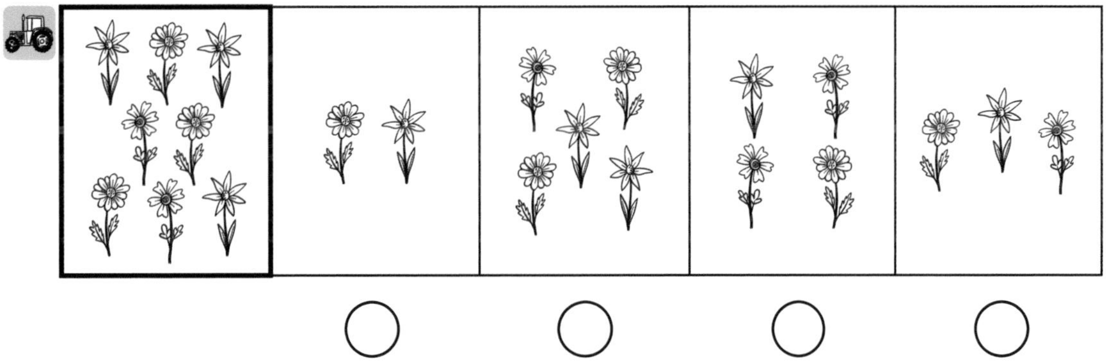

◯   ◯   ◯   ◯

7.

Jill	Jill	Jill	Jill

○   ○   ○   ○

8.

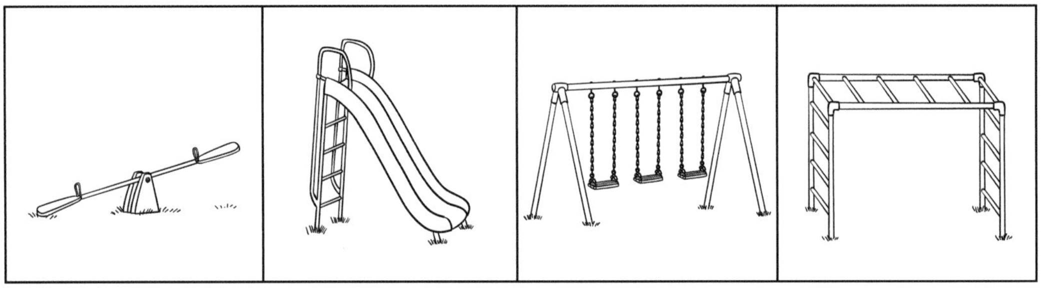

○   ○   ○   ○

9.

A	9	A	8	F
9	C	2	7	4
2	A	8	R	C
8	6	C	3	A

10.

11.

12.

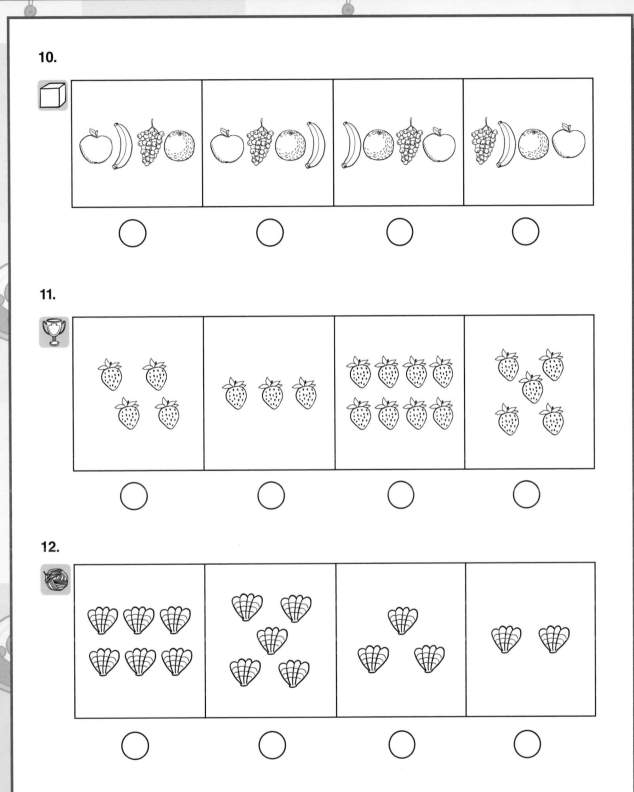

13.

    ◯   ◯   ◯   ◯

14.

    ◯   ◯   ◯   ◯

15.

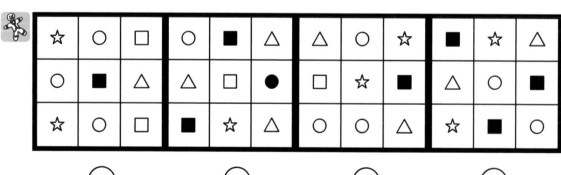

    ◯   ◯   ◯   ◯

16.

17.

18.

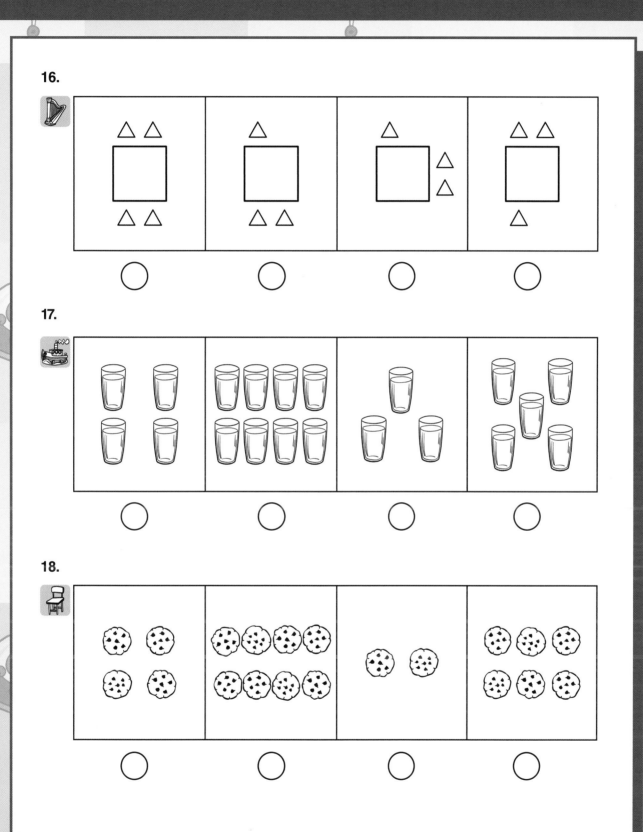

19.

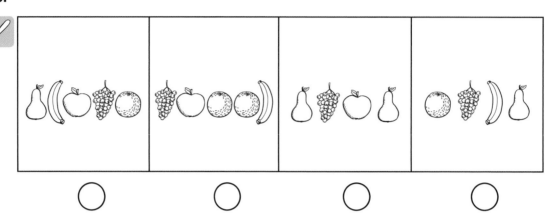

◯   ◯   ◯   ◯

20.

◯   ◯   ◯   ◯

21.

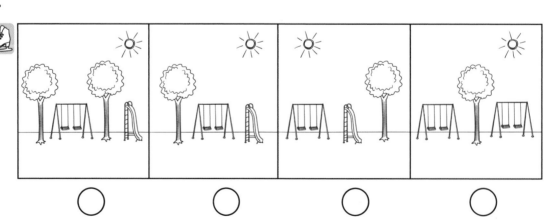

◯   ◯   ◯   ◯

22.

○   ○   ○   ○

23.

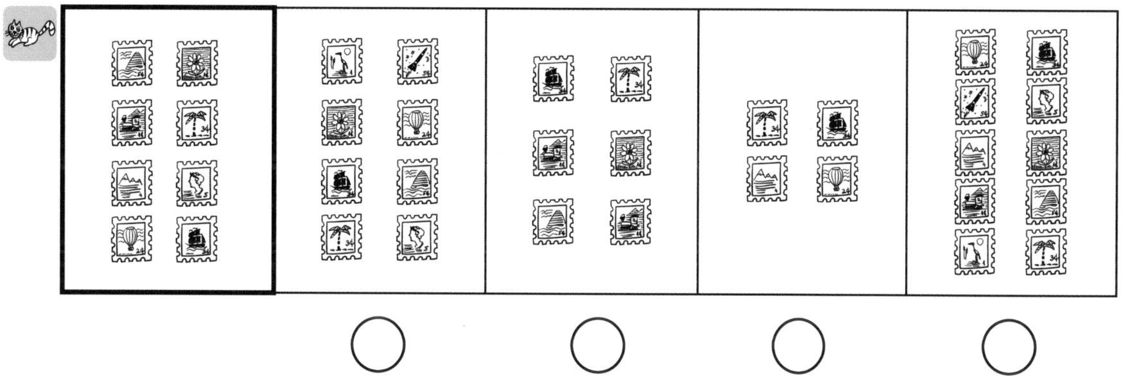

○   ○   ○   ○

24.

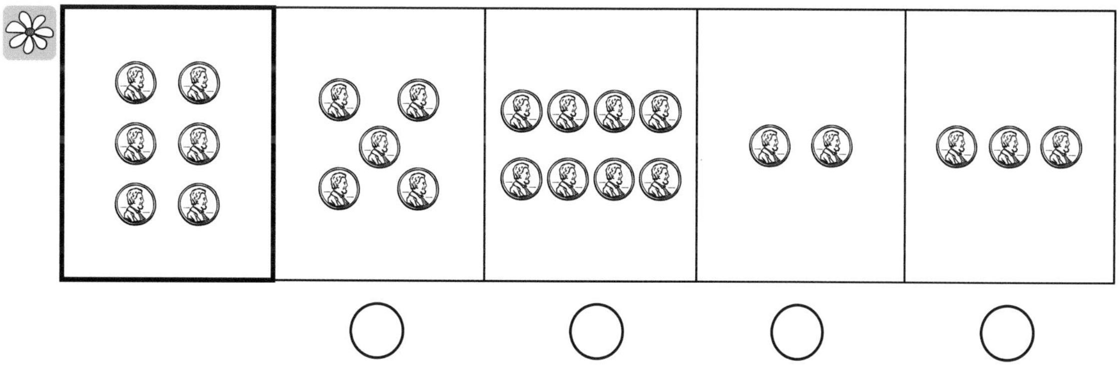

○   ○   ○   ○

25.

○   ○   ○   ○

26.

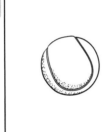   

○   ○   ○   ○

27.

	1			2
1		4	3	H
B			A	
☆	5	□	7	●

28.

29.

30.

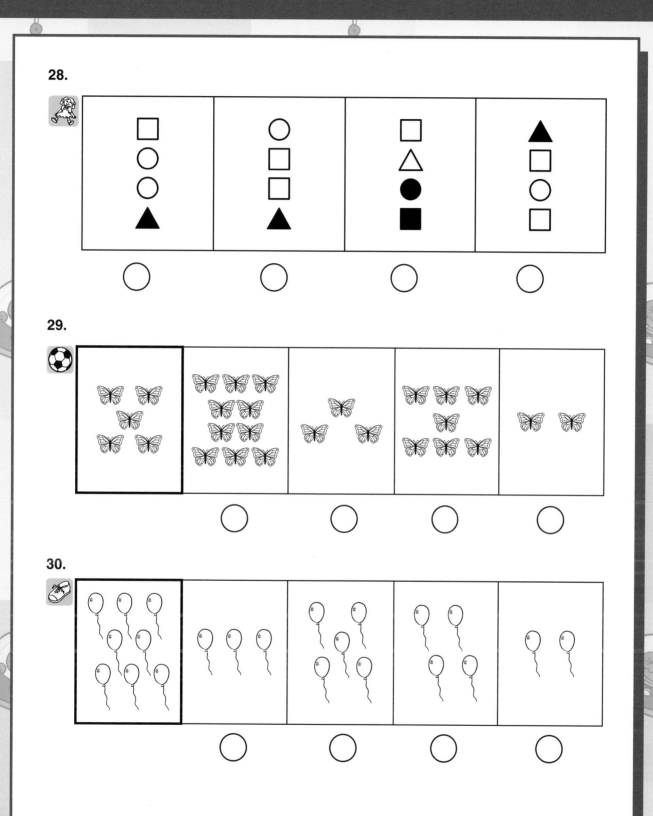